BRAHMS

Two Rhapsodies

Op.79

Edited & annotated by

HOWARD FERGUSON

THE ASSOCIATED BOARD OF
THE ROYAL SCHOOLS OF MUSIC

CONTENTS

Two Rhapsodies, Op.79

INTRODUCTION

Johannes Brahms
(1833-1897)

The solo piano music of Brahms falls into three fairly distinct groups: (1) Three early, romantic Sonatas (C major, Op.1; F sharp minor, Op.2, which was actually the first; and F minor, Op.5), plus the isolated Scherzo in E flat minor, Op.4. (2) Five slightly later, self-disciplining sets of Variations. (3) Seven groups of shorter pieces that make up the present series of volumes, all being late except the *Four Ballads*, Op.10.

Besides these, pianists should not overlook the five splendid works for two players on one piano: *Variations on a theme by Schumann*, Op.23; 16 *Waltzes*, Op.39 (also published in two solo piano versions, simplified and difficult, made by Brahms himself); *Liebeslieder* and *Neue Liebeslieder Waltzes*, Op.52 & 65 (with four optional mixed voices); and 21 *Hungarian Dances*. And also, for two pianos, the *Sonata in F minor*, Op.34b, and *Variations on a theme by Haydn*, Op.56b, the composer's own versions of, respectively, the Piano Quintet in F minor and the well-known Haydn-Variations for orchestra.

SOURCES

Brahms took immense pains to secure accuracy in his published compositions. Furthermore, he kept a copy of the 1st edition of each work and noted in it any mistakes that had been overlooked at the proof stage. (Many works required no correction.) Hence it is these personally corrected copies rather than the autographs that provide the definitive texts of his music. He bequeathed them to the Gesellschaft der Musikfreunde in Vienna; and it is thanks to that Society that it has been possible to use them for the preparation of the present edition.

TEMPO

Brahms' main tempo marks are generally clear and unambiguous. But he used the word *sostenuto* in a special sense, implying a perceptible drop in speed. For example, in the Ballad in G minor, Op.118/3, b.71, *poco sosten.* is followed by *poco a poco in tempo* several bars later. Sometimes *sostenuto sempre* refers to a longer self-contained passage, as in the Rhapsody in B minor, Op.79/1, b.22. Here it undoubtedly remains in force for at least eight bars, and most probably for seventeen, since the vigorous mood of the opening does not return until b.39, where *in tempo* follows a further 2-bar *poco rit.* The duration of a shorter *sostenuto* is generally shown by dashes (*sost. – – –*), with *a tempo* implied (though not indicated) where the dashes cease, as in the Intermezzo in C, Op.119/3, b.10. But note that two

bars later the *sost.* applies to no more than a single quaver.

More rarely a similar drop in tempo is implied by the word *tranquillo*, as in the Capriccio in C sharp minor, Op.76/5, where *poco tranquillo* is shown at b.53, followed by *poco a poco più tranquillo* above bb.58-61, *rit. – – –* above bb.65-68, and finally *Tempo I* at b.69.

Brahms never used metronome marks. When asked for the correct marking for his Rhapsody in B minor, Op.79/1, he replied that he could not give one, as it would be different for every week. And on several occasions he tried (unavailingly) to dissuade Clara Schumann from adding her own metronome marks to the posthumous edition of her husband's complete works.

In spite of this, the present editor has had the temerity to include in his Notes a suggested metronome mark for each piece. It must be understood, however, that it has no authority whatever, and may be ignored if the player so wishes. Far more important is it to remember that Brahms' music generally requires space in which to 'breathe', and will rarely sound right if forced into the straightjacket of a mechanical beat.

FINGERING

Though Brahms only occasionally indicated his own fingering – in these volumes it is always shown in italics – the shape of some of his broken-chord passages shows that they must be fingered in an unusual way. Instead of passing the thumb under the 3rd or 4th finger, or the 3rd or 4th finger over the thumb, the broken-chord is divided into complete handfuls, and the pedal used to mask the break in legato that occurs when jumping from thumb to 5th finger or *vice versa*. For example, in the Capriccio in D minor, Op.116/7, bb.61-63 must be fingered thus:

otherwise the effect of both slurs and accents will be lost. And in the Rhapsody in E flat, Op.119/4, the l.h. passage at bb.39-40 is undoubtedly meant to be fingered:

Many of Brahms' keyboard textures suggest that he had an unusually wide hand-span. Players not similarly blessed should discreetly break chords they cannot stretch, either as quick arpeggios or with the lowest note played as a gracenote before the beat and sustained by pedal.

ARPEGGIOS

An arpeggio sign (⸾) in Brahms often implies a momentary broadening of tempo. In theory the arpeggio should begin on the beat, and it generally does so when in the r.h. alone. If in the l.h. alone it often begins before the beat, its top note coinciding with the beat itself. The overriding consideration, however, must always be to avoid a thin tonal effect; so the player should interpet each arpeggio in the way that seems best suited to its musical context.

PEDALLING

The paired signs, 𝄢. ❋ , indicate no more than the essential use of the sustaining pedal. Elsewhere, and often for a whole piece, Brahms expects the player to supply whatever pedalling may be required. Sometimes the general indication, *col* 𝄢. , appears at the beginning of a piece, as in the Intermezzo in B flat minor, Op.117/2; but it may or may not be followed by anything further. In the same Intermezzo 𝄢. ❋ does in fact appear twice in bb.8-9; yet it is interesting to note that the apparently similar passage at bb.21-22 is left unmarked, in spite of the fact that it needs different pedalling, with a change on beat 3 of the 1st bar (to match the shift in r.h. harmony) instead of on beat 1 of the 2nd bar, as bb.8-9 would suggest. In the Intermezzo in E flat, Op.117/1, the only two indications are *col* 𝄢. at the return of the opening (b.38), and 𝄢. in the penultimate bar; but this of course does not mean that there should be no pedal elsewhere.

Pedalled passages often contain rests and/or staccato marks (*e.g.* in Op.10/3, bb.3-6, and Op.10/2, b.91). Though illogical, this convention is acceptable because the presence of rests may simplify notation, while staccato marks suggest a type of touch or attack which, in conjunction with the pedal, produces a sound perceptibly different from that of a legato.

The sign for the 'soft' pedal, *una corda*, is rare; but it too may be supplemented by the player, so long as he doesn't get into the habit of adding it whenever he sees a ***p***. Sometimes it is cancelled by the words *tre corde* or *tutte corde*, and sometimes the cancellation is left to the player's discretion, as in the Intermezzo in B flat already mentioned.

THIS EDITION

In the present edition numbered footnotes are concerned with textual matters and lettered footnotes with points of interpretation. Editorial accidentals, rests, dynamics, etc., are printed either in small type or within square brackets, and editorial slurs are crossed with a small vertical stroke. Curved brackets indicate that a note should not be struck. Brahms' fingering is shown in italics and the editor's in arabic numerals. Occasionally the editor has altered the distribution of notes on the stave, or employed the signs ⌐ and ⌐ (indicating respectively left hand and right hand), when this might make the text easier to read.

Warmest thanks are due to the Gesellschaft der Musikfreunde, Vienna, for providing microfilms of the 1st editions containing Brahms' corrections; to the Pendelbury Library, Cambridge, for allowing access to other 1st editions; and to both authorities for giving permission for the use of this material in preparing the present texts.

HOWARD FERGUSON
Cambridge 1985

EDITORIAL NOTES

The *Two Rhapsodies* were composed in 1879 during Brahms' summer stay in Pörtschach, and were first published as *Zwei Rhapsodien*, Op.79; N. Simrock, Berlin 1880, Pl.No.8166. In the autograph (now lost) which he sent to the dedicatee, Elizabet von Herzogenberg, the first piece was entitled 'Capriccio'. In his own copy of the 1st edition Brahms made minor alterations to the coda of No.1, but later cancelled them.

1 RHAPSODY IN B MINOR

Agitato [♩ = c.72];
sostenuto sempre (b.22) [♩ = c.56];
b.94 [♩ = c.56]

Two tempi alternate: the faster one for each appearance of the stormy principal subject, and the more relaxed for the reflective contrasting sections (bb.22-38, 94-131, 153-169 & 220*f*).

In bb.16-21 the lowest bass notes have no staccato marks and can therefore be enriched by a touch of pedal. Elsewhere pedalling generally coincides with changes of harmony. The four chromatically ascending crotchets in l.h. b.24 & r.h. b.25 are important because of their later development in bb.44-48, etc.

Though no change of speed is marked for the central section in the major (bb.94-131), there can be no doubt that the slower of the two tempi is intended since it is a development of the earlier D minor theme (b.30*f*). The unexpected bar-structure of its two 'halves' is as follows:

‖: 5 + 2 + 3 :‖: 2 + 2 + 5 + 2 + 7 :‖

In bb.118-121 be careful not to land with a bump on the l.h. low F-sharps. Take them with the 4th finger rather than the 5th, and think of them as stretches (keeping the hand close to the keys) rather than leaps.

In the coda (b.224*f*) let the r.h. triplets float smoothly above the more prominent theme in the l.h. upper line. It is advisable to play l.h. beats 1-2 of bb.228-230 as shown in footnote (*b*), otherwise the necessary change of pedal on beat 2 will lose the bass note B. In bb.233-236 the paired crotchets in r.h. and l.h. are more important than the triplets that continue the textural background begun in b.224.

2 RHAPSODY IN G MINOR

Molto passionato, ma non troppo allegro [♩ = c.108];
b.14, etc [♩ = c.96]

Again two tempi alternate, though they are less strongly contrasted than in No.1 and the second is unmarked. The change is implied, however, because more space is required for the lyrical second theme (bb.14-20) and the dark-hued third (bb.21-32) than for the forthright first. In bb.1 & 2 of the latter the r.h. unison crotchet and dotted-minim are ambiguous, for they could mean that the melodic line of bb.1-3, etc., is either

with the l.h. two-note interpolations slightly less prominent than r.h. beats 4 & 1. The altered layout of bb.65-80, with r.h. beats 4 & 1 as octaves and l.h. beats 2 & 3 as single notes, suggests that the second alternative was probably intended; and certainly bb.35-36, etc., contain two distinct overlapping parts:

(Note that on beat 4 of the 1st of these bars, and beats 2 & 4 of the 2nd, the lower crotchet on the treble stave is taken by the r.h. 4th finger, and the upper crotchet by the l.h. 2nd.)

In the coda the *quasi rit.* at b.118 implies that the passage should slow down gradually, not that the triplets and duplets should be clearly differentiated.

TWO RHAPSODIES
Op. 79

BRAHMS

Agitato

(a) m.v. = mezza voce

(c) Play l.h. beats 1-2 of bb. 228-230 thus:

Molto passionato, ma non troppo allegro

(a) m.g.=main gauche (left hand)

(b) m.v. = mezza voce

AB 1960

Printed in England by Caligraving Limited Thetford Norfolk

10:01